NUMERACY FOR AGES **8-9** Ten Minute Tests

CONTENTS

Paul Broadbent and Peter Patilla

Thousands	Hundreds	Tens	Units	
4	9	5	7	= 4000 + 900 + 50 + 7

Colour in your score on the testometer!

Write the missing numbers.

1. 4173 = 4000 + 100 + ☐ + 3

2. 8465 = ☐ + 400 + 60 + 5

3. 3657 = 3000 + ☐ + 50 + 7

4. 7895 = 7000 + 800 + ☐ + 5

5. 6218 = ☐ + 200 + 10 + 8

Write these as numbers.

6. two thousand one hundred and eight

7. four thousand and ninety

8. seven thousand two hundred and thirty-five

9. three thousand eight hundred and sixteen

10. nine thousand seven hundred

Knowing **number facts** can help you to work out other calculations.

Colour in your score on the testometer!

7 + 6 = 13
70 + 60 = 130
700 + 600 = 1300

12 − 6 = 6
120 − 60 = 60
1200 − 600 = 600

Answer these.

1.   40   +   70   =

2.   90   −   30   =

3.   130   −   50   =

4.   600   +   800   =

5.   900   −   400   =

6.   1200   +   500   =

7.   900   +   700   =

8.   170   −   80   =

9.   190   −   120   =

10.   800   +   500   =

1 centimetre = 10 millimetres	1 litre = 1000 millilitres
1cm = 10mm	1l = 1000ml

1 metre = 100 centimetres	1 kilogram = 1000 grams
1m = 100cm	1kg = 1000g

1 kilometre = 1000 metres
1km = 1000m

Colour in your score on the testometer!

Answer these questions.

1. $\frac{1}{2}$ m = ☐ cm   **2.** $\frac{1}{4}$ l = ☐ ml

3. $\frac{1}{2}$ cm = ☐ mm   **4.** $\frac{1}{4}$ kg = ☐ g

5. $\frac{1}{10}$ km = ☐ m

Measure these lines with a ruler.

6. 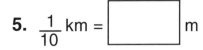 ☐ mm

7.  ☐ mm

8. _____ ☐ mm

9. ☐ mm

10. _____ ☐ mm

A **polygon** is any 2D shape with straight sides.

 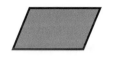

A **regular polygon's** sides and angles are all equal.

Colour in your score on the testometer!

How many sides have each of these shapes?

1. A quadrilateral has sides.

2. An octagon has sides.

3. A hexagon has sides.

4. A triangle has sides.

5. A pentagon has sides.

Name these shapes.

6. _____

7. _____

8. _____

9. _____

10. 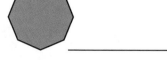 _____

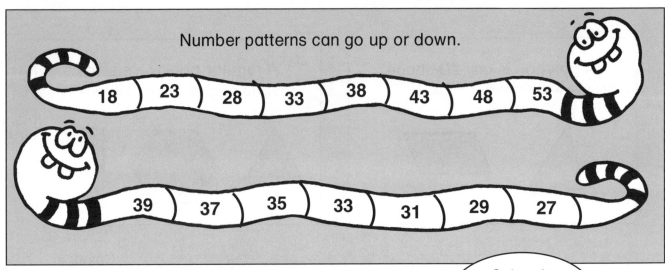

Number patterns can go up or down.

18 23 28 33 38 43 48 53

39 37 35 33 31 29 27

Write the missing numbers in these sequences.

1. | 32 | 35 | 38 | | 44 | 47 | 50 | 53 | | 59 |

2. | 48 | 52 | | 60 | 64 | 68 | | 76 | 80 | 84 |

3. | 31 | 29 | 27 | | 23 | 21 | | 17 | 15 |

4. | 230 | 210 | | 170 | 150 | | 110 | 90 | 70 |

5. | 76 | 81 | 86 | 91 | | 101 | 106 | | 116 |

Write the missing numbers on these number lines.

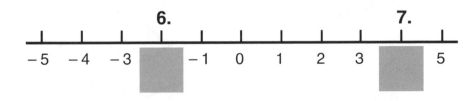

6. 7.

−5 −4 −3 [ ] −1 0 1 2 3 [ ] 5

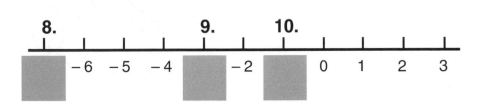

8. 9. 10.

[ ] −6 −5 −4 [ ] −2 [ ] 0 1 2 3

Colour in your score on the testometer!

10
9
8
7
6
5
4
3
2
1

You need to know your **tables**.
Remember, **4 x 6** is the same as **6 x 4**.
It doesn't matter which way round
you multiply.

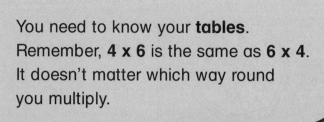

Colour in your score on the testometer!

Write the missing number.

1. 7 x ▢ = 35

2. ▢ x 4 = 40

3. 8 x 3 = ▢

4. ▢ x 7 = 28

5. 2 x ▢ = 18

6. 8 x ▢ = 40

7. 10 x 6 = ▢

8. ▢ x 3 = 27

9. ▢ x 6 = 36

10. 4 x ▢ = 36

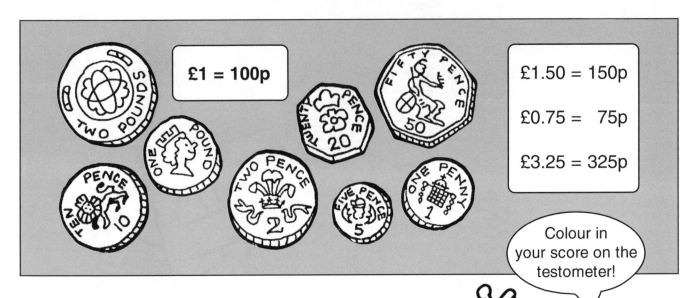

£1 = 100p

£1.50 = 150p

£0.75 = 75p

£3.25 = 325p

Colour in your score on the testometer!

Convert these amounts into pounds or pence.

1. £2.35 = ☐ p

2. £1.09 = ☐ p

3. £6.45 = ☐ p

4. £ ☐ = 214p

5. £ ☐ = 370p

6. £2.75 = ☐ p

Write the totals.

7. £1.85 • > 70p • > £ ☐

8. 65p • > £2.50 • > £ ☐

9. 90p • > £3.15 • > £ ☐

10. £1.90 • > £2.20 • > £ ☐

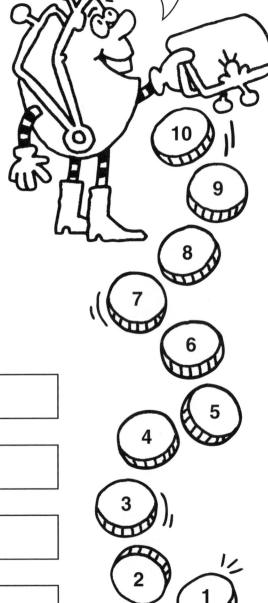

Fractions which are the same value are called **equivalent fractions.**

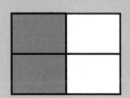   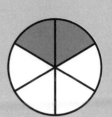

$\dfrac{2}{4}$ is the same as $\dfrac{1}{2}$ $\dfrac{1}{3}$ is the same as $\dfrac{2}{6}$

Write the fractions which are shaded.

1. 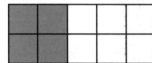 $\dfrac{\Box}{10} = \dfrac{\Box}{5}$

2. $\dfrac{\Box}{6} = \dfrac{\Box}{2}$

Colour in your score on the testometer!

3. 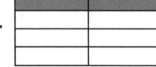 $\dfrac{\Box}{8} = \dfrac{\Box}{4}$

4.  $\dfrac{\Box}{8} = \dfrac{\Box}{4}$

5. $\dfrac{\Box}{8} = \dfrac{\Box}{2}$

Complete these fractions.

6. $\dfrac{4}{5} = \dfrac{8}{\Box}$ **7.** $\dfrac{2}{3} = \dfrac{\Box}{9}$ **8.** $\dfrac{1}{\Box} = \dfrac{3}{12}$

9. $\dfrac{3}{4} = \dfrac{\Box}{12}$ **10.** $\dfrac{3}{10} = \dfrac{6}{\Box}$

10
9
8
7
6
5
4
3
2
1

Choc

Choc

Mornings and **afternoons** are shown by **am** and **pm**.

7.25am ⟶ this is in the morning.

7.25pm ⟶ this is in the evening.

Aston	9.55am	10.45am	11.50am
Banley	10.25am	11.20am	12.25pm
Compton	10.40am	11.40am	12.50pm
Dinsford	11.30am	12.20pm	1.45pm

11.35

hours   minutes past the hour

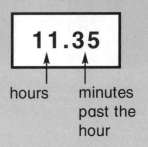

How many minutes do these train journeys take?

Colour in your score on the testometer!

1.   9.55am Aston ➜ Banley [   ] minutes

2.   11.20am Banley ➜ Compton [   ] minutes

3.   12.50pm Compton ➜ Dinsford [   ] minutes

4.   10.45am Aston ➜ Compton [   ] minutes

5.   10.25am Banley ➜ Dinsford [   ] minutes

Draw the hands on each clock to show the time

6.   8.55

7.   3.45

8.   10.35

9.   12.40

10.   1.05

This **pictogram** shows information about 4 buses that make the same journey at different times.

Bus	Number of people on each bus
A	☆ ☆ ⭒
B	☆ ☆
C	☆ ☆ ☆ ☆ ☆ ⭒
D	☆ ☆ ☆

☆ 5 people

⭒ between 1 and 5 people

Passengers on bus C

Adults	Children	Babies

☺☺ = 2 people   ☺ = 1 person

1. How many people travelled on bus B? ▢

2. How many people travelled on bus D? ▢

3. Approximately how many people travelled on bus A?

   Between ▢ and ▢

4. Approximately how many people travelled on bus C?

   Between ▢ and ▢

5. Approximately how many people travelled altogether on all 4 buses?

   Between ▢ and ▢

6. How many adults travelled on bus C? ▢

7. How many children travelled on bus C? ▢

8. How many babies travelled on bus C? ▢

9. How many more adults than children travelled on bus C? ▢

10. How many people travelled altogether on bus C? ▢

Colour in your score on the testometer!

To **multiply by 10**, move all the digits to the **left**. The empty place is filled by a zero.

$$75 \times 10 =$$
↓↓
750

To **divide by 10**, move all the digits one place to the **right**.

$$230 \div 10 =$$
↓↓
23

Colour in your score on the testometer!

Multiply each of these numbers by 10.

1. 45 ⊏ x 10 ⇨ ☐

2. 63 ⊏ x 10 ⇨ ☐

3. 81 ⊏ x 10 ⇨ ☐

4. 107 ⊏ x 10 ⇨ ☐

5. 234 ⊏ x 10 ⇨ ☐

Divide each of these numbers by 10.

6. 530 ⊏ ÷10 ⇨ ☐

7. 470 ⊏ ÷10 ⇨ ☐

8. 380 ⊏ ÷10 ⇨ ☐

9. 6350 ⊏ ÷10 ⇨ ☐

10. 8010 ⊏ ÷10 ⇨ ☐

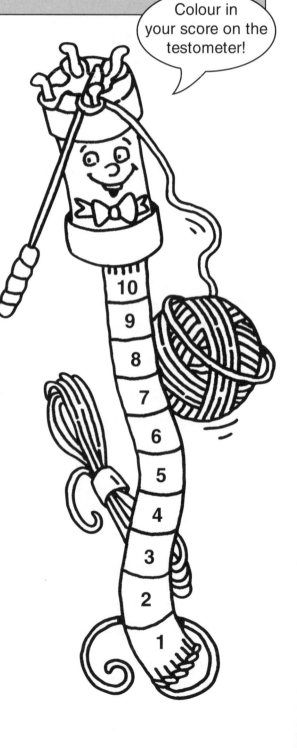

Use mental methods to answer these.

1. 48 + 30 =

2. 36 + 23 =

3. 44 + 46 =

4. 38 + 70 =

5. 56 + 29 =

6. 48 + 37 =

7. 81 + 63 =

8. 72 + 49 =

9. 39 + 45 =

10. 57 + 74 =

Test 13 — Money: adding coins

When adding coins, start with the **highest value** coins to make it easier.

Colour in your score on the testometer!

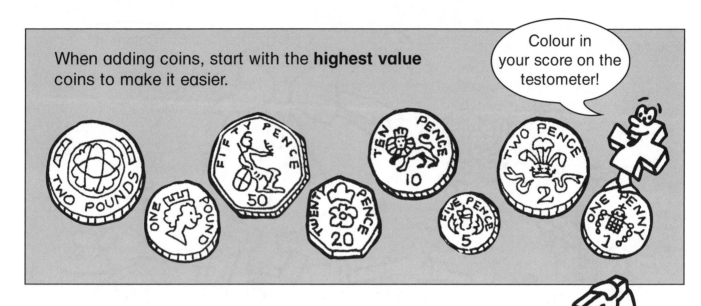

Write these totals. Start with the highest value.

1. £1 20p 20p 50p 2p ⇨ [ ]

2. £1 £1 20p 50p 10p ⇨ [ ]

3. 50p 20p £2 2p 5p ⇨ [ ]

4. 10p 1p 2p £2 £2 ⇨ [ ]

5. 10p 50p 2p 5p £1 ⇨ [ ]

Which coins would you use to buy these books.

6. £4.90 _____

7. £3.50 _____

8. £1.13 _____

9. £2.26 _____

10. £4.14 _____

When doing **measures problems**, make sure you read the questions carefully and then work out what calculations you need to do.

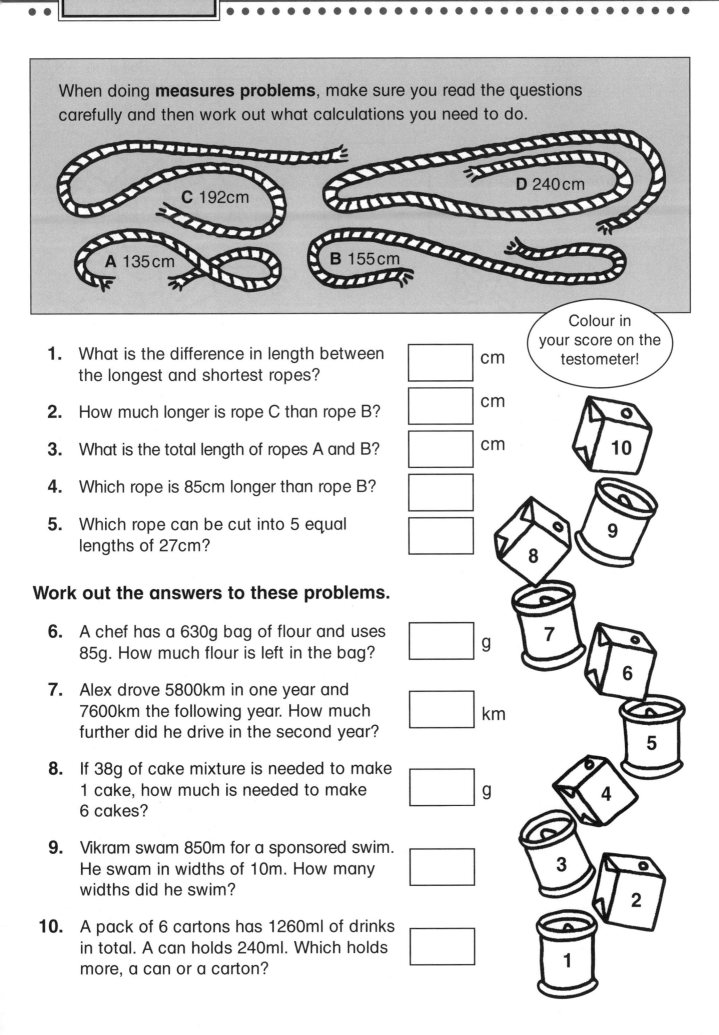

C 192cm

D 240cm

A 135cm

B 155cm

1. What is the difference in length between the longest and shortest ropes? ☐ cm

Colour in your score on the testometer!

2. How much longer is rope C than rope B? ☐ cm

3. What is the total length of ropes A and B? ☐ cm

4. Which rope is 85cm longer than rope B? ☐

5. Which rope can be cut into 5 equal lengths of 27cm? ☐

Work out the answers to these problems.

6. A chef has a 630g bag of flour and uses 85g. How much flour is left in the bag? ☐ g

7. Alex drove 5800km in one year and 7600km the following year. How much further did he drive in the second year? ☐ km

8. If 38g of cake mixture is needed to make 1 cake, how much is needed to make 6 cakes? ☐ g

9. Vikram swam 850m for a sponsored swim. He swam in widths of 10m. How many widths did he swim? ☐

10. A pack of 6 cartons has 1260ml of drinks in total. A can holds 240ml. Which holds more, a can or a carton? ☐

These are the parts of a **3 dimensional** (3D) shape.

A cube has:
   8 corners (vertices)
12 edges
   6 faces

vertex
edge
face

Colour in your score on the testometer!

Name each shape. Write the missing numbers of corners, edges or faces.

1. name _____

2. [ ] corners   [8] edges   **3.** [ ] faces

4. name _____

5. [0] corners   **5.** [ ] edges   **6.** [ ] faces

7. name _____

7. [1] corners   [1] edges   **8.** [ ] faces

9. name _____

[8] corners   [12] edges   **10.** [ ] faces

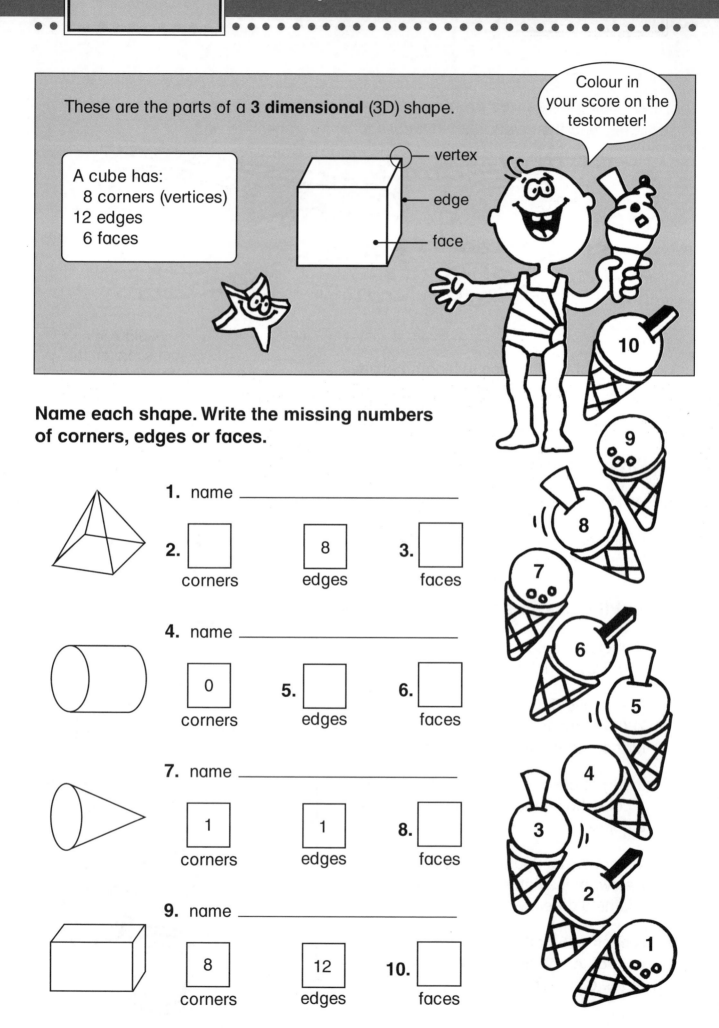

Look for number patterns.

1	2	3	4	5	6
7	8	9	10	11	12
13	14	15	16	17	18
19	20	21	22	23	24
25	26	27	28	29	30
31	32	33	34	35	36

Colour in your score on the testometer!

Write the next number in each number pattern.

1. | 12 | 14 | 16 | 18 | 20 | |

2. | 15 | 18 | 21 | 24 | 27 | |

3. | 9 | 11 | 13 | 15 | 17 | |

4. | 33 | 30 | 27 | 24 | 21 | |

5. | 16 | 20 | 24 | 28 | 32 | |

Write the missing number in each number pattern.

6. 22 — 20 — 18 — ◯ — 14 — 12 — 10

7. 27 — 24 — ◯ — 18 — 15 — 12 — 9

8. ◯ — 28 — 30 — 32 — 34 — 36 — 38

9. 36 — 32 — 28 — ◯ — 20 — 16 — 12

10. 9 — 12 — 15 — 18 — ◯ — 24 — 27

10
9
8
7
6
5
4
3
2
1

Use multiplication to help work out **division** questions.

$24 \div 6 = \boxed{}$ ⇨ $6 \times \boxed{} = 24$

$6 \times 4 = 24$

⇩

$24 \div 6 = 4$

If a number cannot be divided exactly, it leaves a remainder.

$26 \div 4 = 6$ remainder 2

Colour in your score on the testometer!

Answer these.

1. $30 \div 5 =$

2. $32 \div 4 =$

3. $42 \div 3 =$

4. $52 \div 2 =$

5. $85 \div 5 =$

Answer these and write the remainder.

6. $34 \div 4 =$ ___ remainder ___

7. $29 \div 2 =$ ___ remainder ___

8. $58 \div 5 =$ ___ remainder ___

9. $47 \div 3 =$ ___ remainder ___

10. $86 \div 10 =$ ___ remainder ___

When finding the **difference** between two amounts,
count on from the **lower** amount.

The **difference** between £1.80 and £3.30 is **£1.50** (20p + £1 + 30p).

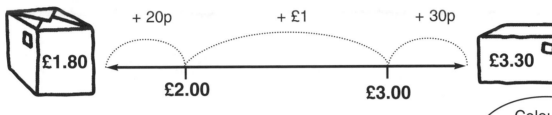

Colour in your score on the testometer!

Write the difference between these prices.

1.  £2.40 £3.50

2.  £1.70 £2.25

3.  £2.40 £1.60

4. £2.34 £1.50

5. £1.95 £1.10

6. £3.45 £2.90

7. £4.72 £2.80

8. £1.30 £4.65

9. £2.63 £1.20

10.  £4.18 £2.80

$\frac{1}{3}$ of 15 **is the same as** 15 ÷ 3 = 5

Work out the answers.

1. $\frac{1}{4}$ of   12   =

2. $\frac{1}{2}$ of   28   =

3. $\frac{1}{3}$ of   18   =

4. $\frac{1}{5}$ of   20   =

5. $\frac{1}{4}$ of   16   =

6. $\frac{1}{10}$ of   60   =

7. $\frac{1}{3}$ of   24   =

8. $\frac{1}{5}$ of   35   =

9. $\frac{1}{4}$ of   32   =

10. $\frac{1}{10}$ of   90   =

Colour in your score on the testometer!

The numbers 1-10 have been sorted on these two diagrams.

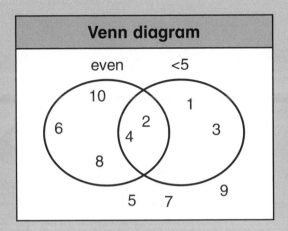

Venn diagram	Carroll diagram

Venn diagram:
even   <5
10   6   8   (2, 4)   1   3   5   7   9

Carroll diagram:

	even	not even
<5	2 4	1 3
not <5	6 10 8	5 9 7

Colour in your score on the testometer!

Write the numbers in the correct place on each diagram.

>   means greater than
<   means less than

1.   7

2.   31

3.   28

4.   16

5.   19

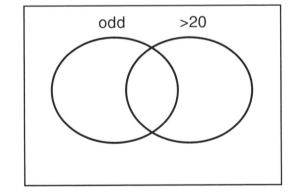

odd   >20

6.   24

7.   13

8.   15

9.   1

10.   6

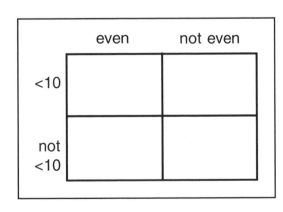

	even	not even
<10		
not <10		

To help work out the **order of numbers**, you can write them in a list, lining up the units columns.

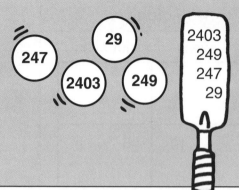

> greater than
< less than

Colour in your score on the testometer!

Write the signs > or < for each pair of numbers.

1. 6093 ☐ 6103   **2.** 2046 ☐ 2050

3. 4206 ☐ 4311   **4.** 8114 ☐ 8108

5. 7415 ☐ 7409

Write the numbers in order starting with the smallest.

6.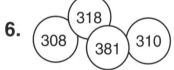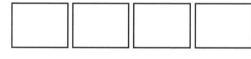

7.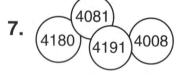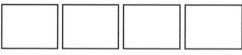

8.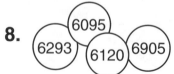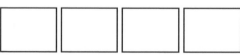

9.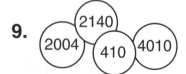

10.

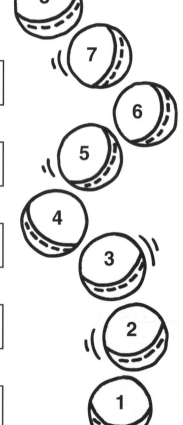

There are lots of ways to **take one number from another**. Use mental methods to work them out in your head.

Colour in your score on the testometer!

Use mental methods to answer these.

1.   42   –   29   =

2.   57   –   23   =

3.   31   –   17   =

4.   62   –   31   =

5.   54   –   19   =

6.   81   –   4   =

7.   305   –   9   =

8.   63   –   38   =

9.   52   –   7   =

10.   89   –   35   =

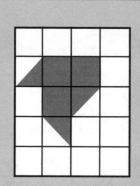 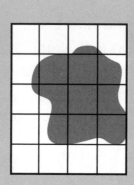

To work out the area of an **irregular shape,** count the whole squares.

$\frac{1}{2}$ or more squares count as whole squares.

Ignore squares less than $\frac{1}{2}$.

For shapes with **straight sides**, count $\frac{1}{2}$ squares.

Colour in your score on the testometer!

Work out the areas of these shapes.

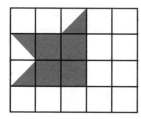 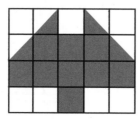 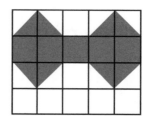

1. ☐ squares **2.** ☐ squares **3.** ☐ squares

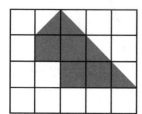 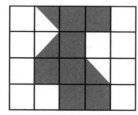 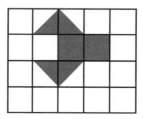

4. ☐ squares **5.** ☐ squares **6.** ☐ squares

Work out the approximate areas of these shapes.

7. **8.** **9.** **10.**

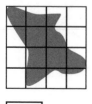   

☐ squares ☐ squares ☐ squares ☐ squares

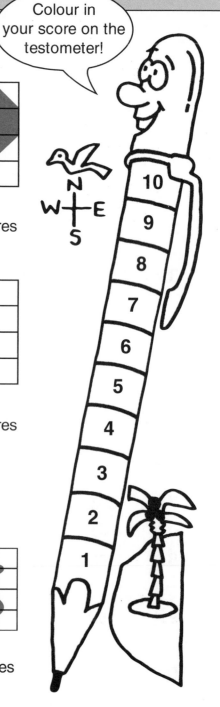

Test 24 — Shape: symmetry

A shape has line **symmetry** if both sides are exactly the same when a mirror line is drawn.

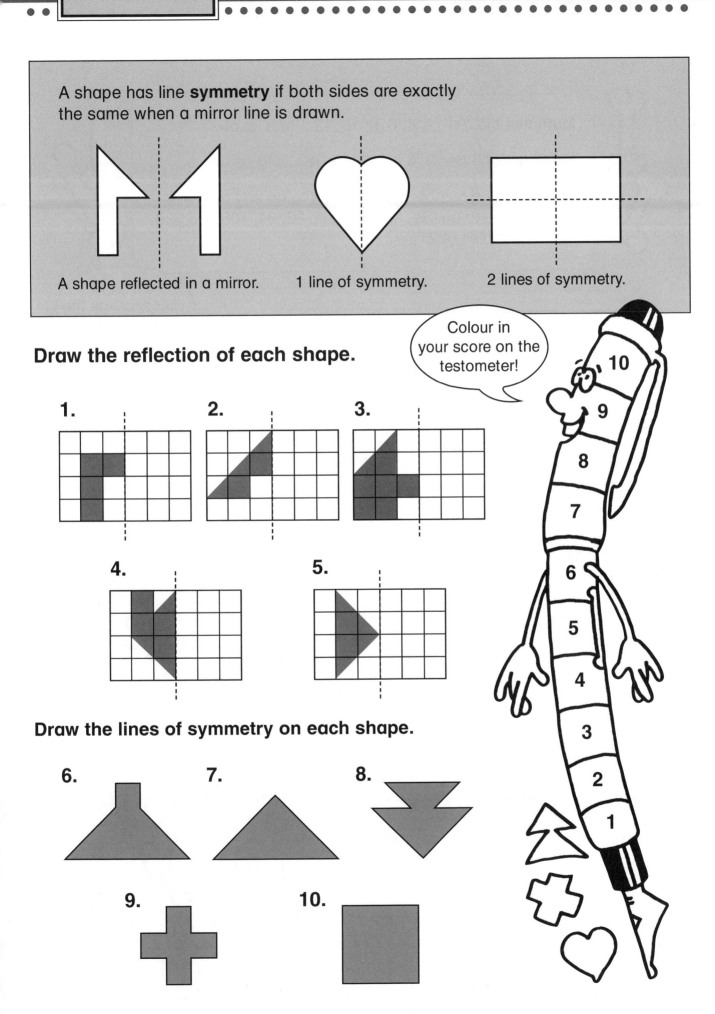

A shape reflected in a mirror.

1 line of symmetry.

2 lines of symmetry.

Draw the reflection of each shape.

Colour in your score on the testometer!

1.

2.

3.

4.

5.

Draw the lines of symmetry on each shape.

6.

7.

8.

9.

10.

Multiples of 2 are: 2, 4, 6, 8, 10, 12... and so on.

Multiples of 3 are: 3, 6, 9, 12, 15, 18... and so on.

Multiples of a number do not come to an end at x10, they go on and on. So, for example, 82, 94, 106 and 300 are all multiples of 2.

Colour in your score on the testometer!

Which of these numbers are multiples of 2, 3, 4 or 5? Some numbers are used more than once.

36   110   65   99   92   111

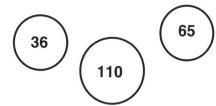

Multiples of 2

1.

2.

3.

Multiples of 3

4.

5.

6.

Multiples of 4

7.

8.

Multiples of 5

9.

10.

When **multiplying** it can help to break numbers up.

43 x 5 =

40 x 5	=	200
3 x 5	=	+ 15
43 x 5	=	215

```
    4 3
  x   5
  -----
  2 1 5
      1
```

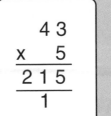

Colour in your score on the testometer!

Answer these.

1. 36 x 3 =

2. 41 x 4 =

3. 53 x 2 =

4. 47 x 3 =

5. 56 x 4 =

Answer these.

6. 53
    x 3
    ____

7. 84
    x 2
    ____

8. 67
    x 4
    ____

9. 74
    x 3
    ____

10. 59
    x 5
    ____

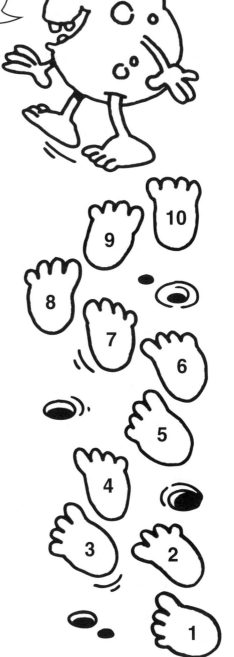

When working out **word problems**, read the questions carefully to work out the calculations you need to do.

Colour in your score on the testometer!

Answer these problems.

1. Amy has 95p and spends 57p. How much money does she have left?

2. A cinema ticket costs £3.50 for an adult and £3 for a child. What is the total cost for 2 adults and 2 children?

3. A newspaper costs 35p. What is the cost for a week's supply of newspapers?

4. A sweet costs 14p. How many can be bought for £1?

5. A bus journey costs £1.20. How much will the total fare be for 4 people?

6. A car costs £2400. If it is reduced by £800, how much will it cost?

7. A book costs £4.70. It is reduced by £1.90 in a sale. What is the new price of the book?

8. Sam has two 20p coins and a 50p coin. He buys a magazine at 72p. How much money does he have left?

9. What is the total cost of a £4.50 T-shirt and a £3.70 pair of shorts?

10. If a fairground ride costs 80p, what is the cost of 3 rides?

PRIZES

A **decimal point** is used to separate whole numbers from fractions.

$$0 \cdot 1 = \frac{1}{10}$$

$$0 \cdot 2 = \frac{2}{10}$$

$$0 \cdot 5 = \frac{1}{2}$$

tens	units	tenths
8	**2** ·	**6**
80	2	$\frac{6}{10}$

Change these fractions to decimals.

1. $\frac{7}{10}$ = ☐

2. $1\frac{1}{2}$ = ☐

3. $3\frac{3}{10}$ = ☐

4. $\frac{9}{10}$ = ☐

5. $2\frac{4}{10}$ = ☐

Colour in your score on the testometer!

Write the decimals on this number line.

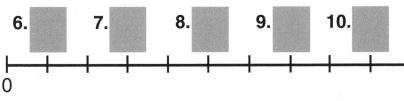

6. ☐ 7. ☐ 8. ☐ 9. ☐ 10. ☐

0 ———————————————— 1

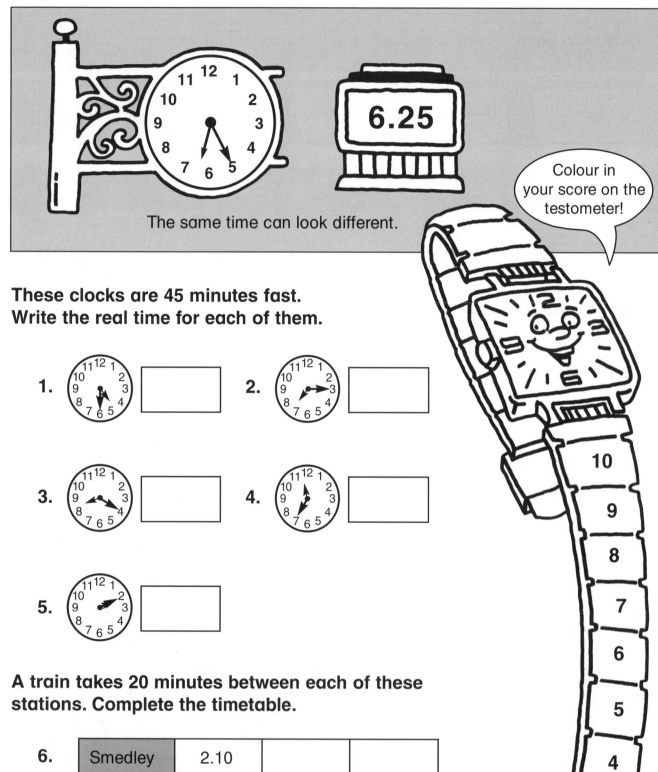

The same time can look different.

Colour in your score on the testometer!

These clocks are 45 minutes fast.
Write the real time for each of them.

1. ☐

2. ☐

3. ☐

4. ☐

5. ☐

A train takes 20 minutes between each of these stations. Complete the timetable.

6.	Smedley	2.10		
7.	Chadwick		4.45	
8.	Welby	2.50		
9.	Burnsford			7.55
10.	Ragby		5.45	

These **graphs** show the number of cans collected by two classes in a school over a month.

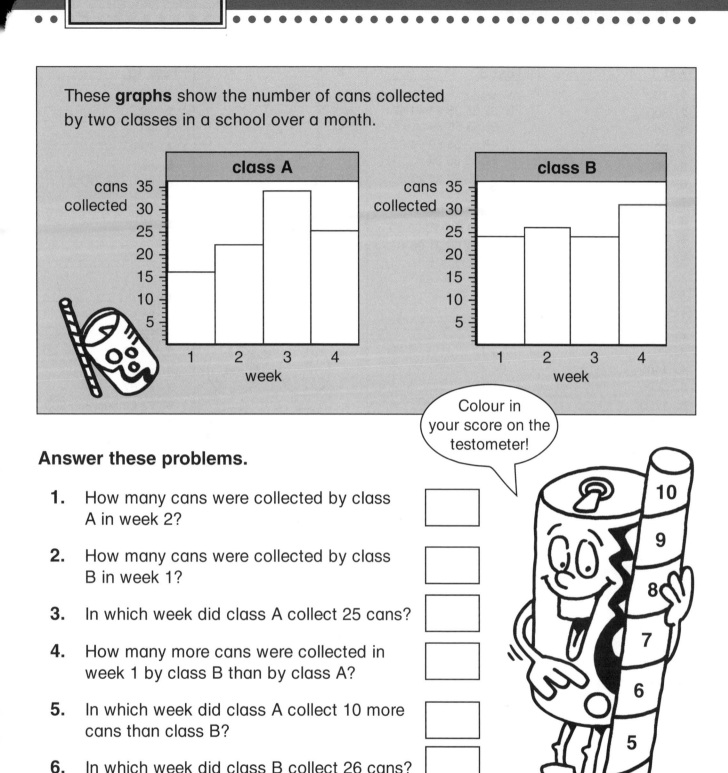

Answer these problems.

1. How many cans were collected by class A in week 2?

2. How many cans were collected by class B in week 1?

3. In which week did class A collect 25 cans?

4. How many more cans were collected in week 1 by class B than by class A?

5. In which week did class A collect 10 more cans than class B?

6. In which week did class B collect 26 cans?

7. In which 2 weeks were the same number of cans collected by class B?

8. How many more cans were collected in week 3 by class A than by class B?

9. How many cans altogether were collected by class B?

10. Which class collected the most cans?

Colour in your score on the testometer!

Answers

Test 1
1. 70
2. 8000
3. 600
4. 90
5. 6000
6. 2108
7. 4090
8. 7235
9. 3816
10. 9700

Test 2
1. 110
2. 60
3. 80
4. 1400
5. 500
6. 1700
7. 1600
8. 90
9. 70
10. 1300

Test 3
1. 50cm
2. 250ml
3. 5mm
4. 250g
5. 100m
6. 38mm
7. 52mm
8. 63mm
9. 26mm
10. 77mm

Test 4
1. 4
2. 8
3. 6
4. 3
5. 5
6. pentagon
7. quadrilateral
8. hexagon
9. triangle
10. octagon

Test 5
The missing numbers are in **bold**.
1. 32 35 38 **41** 44 47 50 53 **56** 59
2. 48 52 **56** 60 64 68 **72** 76 80 84
3. 31 29 27 **25** 23 21 **19** 17 15
4. 230 210 **190** 170 150 **130** 110 90 70
5. 76 81 86 91 **96** 101 106 **111** 116
6. − 2
7. 4
8. − 7
9. − 3
10. − 1

Test 6
1. 5
2. 10
3. 24
4. 4
5. 9
6. 5
7. 60
8. 9
9. 6
10. 9

Test 7
1. 235p
2. 109p
3. 645p
4. £2.14
5. £3.70
6. 275p
7. £2.55
8. £3.15
9. £4.05
10. £4.10

Test 8
1. $\frac{4}{10} = \frac{2}{5}$
2. $\frac{3}{6} = \frac{1}{2}$
3. $\frac{2}{8} = \frac{1}{4}$
4. $\frac{6}{8} = \frac{3}{4}$
5. $\frac{4}{8} = \frac{1}{2}$
6. $\frac{8}{10}$
7. $\frac{6}{9}$
8. $\frac{1}{4}$
9. $\frac{9}{12}$
10. $\frac{6}{20}$

Test 9
1. 30 minutes
2. 20 minutes
3. 55 minutes
4. 55 minutes
5. 65 minutes

6. 7.

8. 9.

10.

Test 10
1. 10
2. 15
3. Between 11 and 15.
4. Between 26 and 30.
5. Between 57 and 65.
6. 14
7. 9
8. 5
9. 5
10. 28

Test 11
1. 450
2. 630
3. 810
4. 1070
5. 2340
6. 53
7. 47
8. 38
9. 635
10. 801

Test 12
1. 78
2. 59
3. 90
4. 108
5. 85
6. 85
7. 144
8. 121
9. 84
10. 131

Test 13
1. £1.92
2. £2.80
3. £2.77
4. £4.13
5. £1.67
6. £2 £2 50p 20p 20p
7. £2 £1 50p
8. £1 10p 2p 1p
9. £2 20p 5p 1p
10. £2 £2 10p 2p 2p

Test 14
1. 105cm
2. 37cm
3. 290cm
4. D
5. A
6. 545g
7. 1800km
8. 228g
9. 85
10. can

Test 15
1. pyramid
2. 5 corners
3. 5 faces
4. cylinder
5. 2 edges
6. 3 faces
7. cone
8. 2 faces
9. cuboid
10. 6 faces